GW00670505

Electronic Keyboard
Initial

Pieces & Technical Work
for Trinity College London exams

2015-2018

Published by
Trinity College London Press

Registered in England
Company no. 09726123

Copyright © 2014 Trinity College London
Fourth impression, June 2017

Printed in England by Caligraving Ltd.

Own Interpretation*

Ode to Joy

Ludwig van Beethoven
arr. Victoria Proudler

Voice: 001 · PNO
Style: 001 – 8 Beat

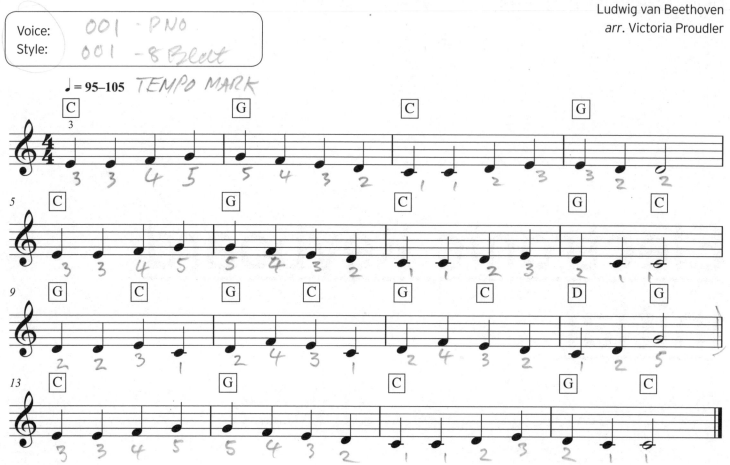

♩ = 95–105 TEMPO MARK

* Candidates should refer to the current syllabus requirements for Own Interpretation pieces.

PLEASE SET UP FOR THE NEXT PIECE

Camptown Races

Stephen Foster
arr. Andrew Smith

Voice: Banjo (sounding octave lower) (115) 115
Style: Bluegrass 058

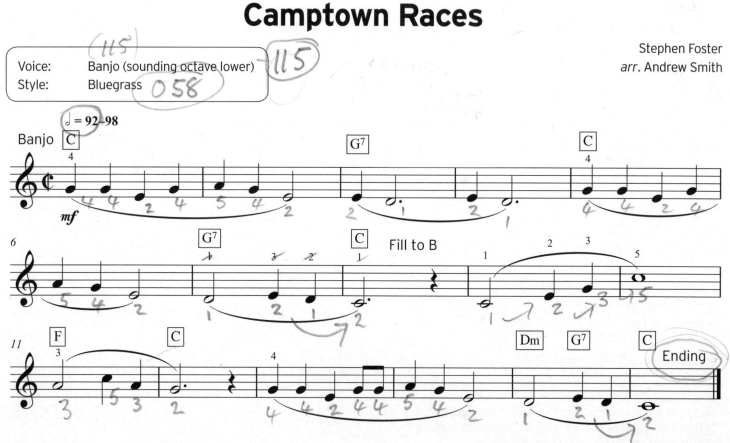

♩ = 92–98

PLEASE SET UP FOR THE NEXT PIECE

Panis Angelicus

César Franck
arr. Nancy Litten

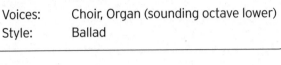

Voices: Choir, Organ (sounding octave lower)
Style: Ballad

PLEASE SET UP FOR THE NEXT PIECE

What Shall We Do with the Drunken Sailor?

Traditional
arr. Victoria Proudler

PLEASE SET UP FOR THE NEXT PIECE

The Keel Row

Traditional
arr. Jeremy Ward

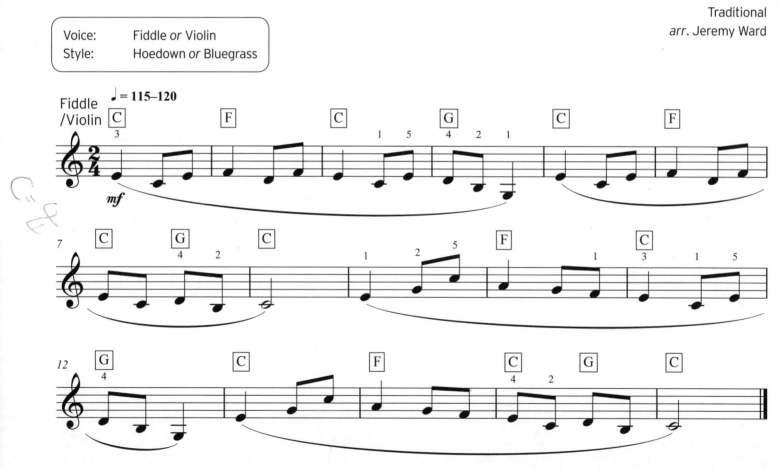

PLEASE SET UP FOR THE NEXT PIECE

Flea Hop

Nancy Litten

Voices: Hop Lead, Pizz. Strings
Style: Hip Hop

PLEASE SET UP FOR THE NEXT PIECE

5

O Sole Mio

Eduardo di Capua

arr. Joanna Clarke

Voices: Accordion, Strings
Style: Tango

PLEASE SET UP FOR THE NEXT PIECE

Country Capers

Andrew Smith

Voice: Steel Drums
Style: Merengue *or* Beguine

Fill to B

Ending

PLEASE SET UP FOR THE NEXT PIECE

My Little Dog

Septimus Winner
arr. Rory Marsden

Voices: Alto Saxophone, Flute
Style: English Waltz

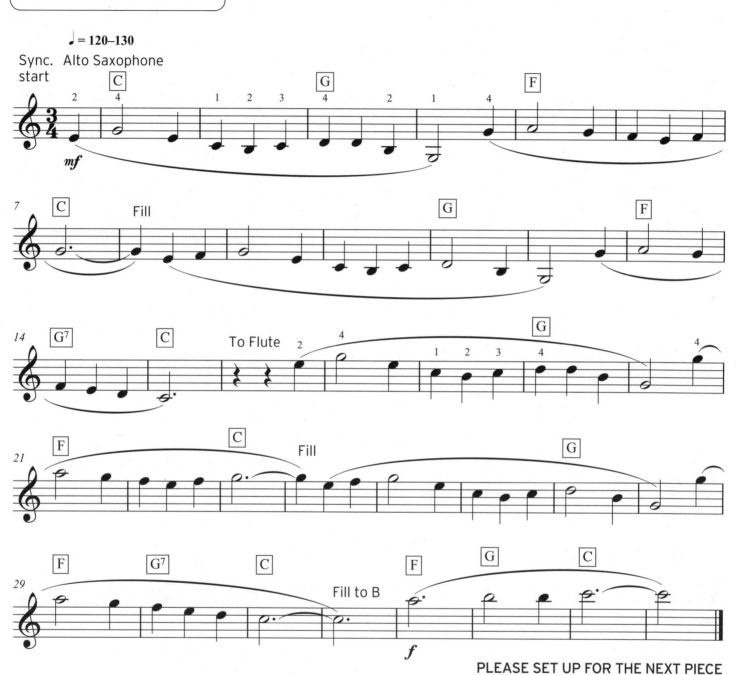

PLEASE SET UP FOR THE NEXT PIECE

Rock to the Roll

Joanna Clarke

Voices: Electric Guitar, Jazz Organ (sounding octave lower)
Style: Rock & Roll *or* Shuffle

PLEASE SET UP FOR THE NEXT PIECE

Technical Work

Technical work – candidates to prepare in full *either* section i) *or* section ii)						
either i) **Scales & chord knowledge** (from memory) – the examiner will select from the following:						
C major A minor (candidate's choice of *either* harmonic *or* melodic *or* natural minor) Pentatonic scale starting on C (5 notes)	min. ♩ = 60	one octave	*legato* and ***mf***	hands separately	piano voice with auto-accompaniment off	
C major contrary motion scale				hands together		
Chromatic scale starting on D				R.H. only		
Triad of C major and A minor (root position)				L.H. only		
or ii) **Exercises** (music may be used):						
Candidates to prepare **all** three exercises. The candidate will choose one exercise to play first; the examiner will then select one of the remaining two exercises to be performed.						
Dreaming			keyboard functions exercise			
Stepping Out			scalic exercise			
Clouds			pianistic exercise			

Please refer to the current syllabus for details on all elements of the exam

i) Scales & chord knowledge

C major scale (one octave)

Right hand

Left hand

A minor scale: harmonic (one octave)

Right hand

Left hand

A minor scale: melodic (one octave)

Right hand

Left hand

A minor scale: natural (one octave)

Right hand

Left hand

Pentatonic scale starting on C (five notes)

Right hand

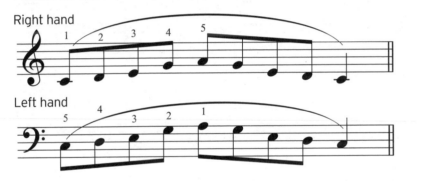

Left hand

C major contrary motion scale (one octave)

Chromatic scale starting on D (one octave)

Right hand

C major   A minor

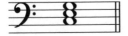   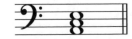

ii) Exercises

1. Dreaming – keyboard functions exercise

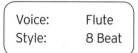

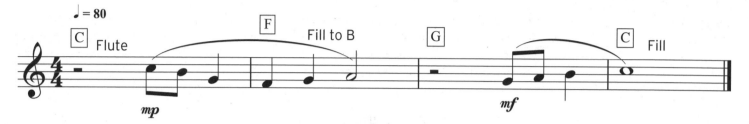

2. Stepping Out – scalic exercise

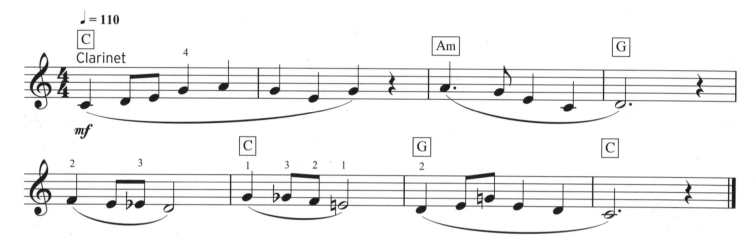

3. Clouds – pianistic exercise

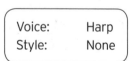

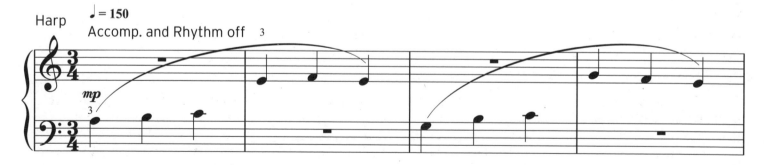